ALBUM II

5 Easy Pieces for Descant (Soprano) Recorder and Basso continuo
by J. S. Bach, M. F. Caroso, H. Purcell, and A. Vivaldi

Edited by
Manfredo Zimmermann

DOWANI International

Preface

This edition offers easy-to-play yet musically challenging arrangements for descant (soprano) recorder and basso continuo. Manfredo Zimmermann, professor of recorder at the Musikhochschule Cologne/Wuppertal and specialist in early music has edited and performed this collection of musical highlights from various countries. The basso continuo accompaniment is set for different instruments in the individual pieces and is performed on harpsichord or organ in the recordings. Our edition enables you to learn the pieces systematically and in three differing tempi with professional accompaniments.

The CD opens with the concert version of each piece, played with recorder and basso continuo. After tuning your instrument (Track 1), the musical work can begin. First, you will hear the basso continuo (or organ) accompaniment at slow and medium tempo for practice purposes. At slow tempo you can also hear the recorder played softly in the background as a guide. Having mastered these levels, you can now play with basso continuo (or organ) accompaniment at the original tempo. All of the versions were recorded live. The names of the musicians are listed on the last page of this volume; further information can be found in the Internet at www.dowani.com.

We wish you lots of fun playing from our *DOWANI 3 Tempi Play Along* editions and hope that your musicality and diligence will enable you to play the concert version as soon as possible. Our goal is to provide the essential conditions you need for effective practicing through motivation, enjoyment and fun.

Your DOWANI Team

Avant-propos

Le présent recueil vous propose des arrangements pour flûte à bec soprano et basse continue qui sont techniquement faciles, mais d'un haut niveau musical. Manfredo Zimmermann, professeur de flûte à bec au Conservatoire Supérieur de Cologne/Wuppertal et spécialiste dans le domaine de la musique ancienne, a édité et enregistré cette collection de morceaux célèbres de plusieurs pays. L'instrumentation de la basse continue est différente pour chaque morceau ; elle a été enregistrée avec clavecin ou bien orgue. Notre édition vous offre la possibilité de travailler les morceaux d'une manière systématique dans trois différents tempos avec un accompagnement professionnel.

Le CD vous permettra d'entendre d'abord la version de concert de chaque morceau (flûte à bec et basse continue). Après avoir accordé votre instrument (plage n° 1), vous pourrez commencer le travail musical. Pour travailler les morceaux au tempo lent et au tempo moyen, vous entendrez l'accompagnement de la basse continue ou bien de l'orgue. Au tempo lent, la flûte à bec restera cependant toujours audible très doucement à l'arrière-plan. Vous pourrez ensuite jouer le tempo original avec accompagnement de la basse continue ou bien de l'orgue. Toutes les versions ont été enregistrées en direct. Vous trouverez les noms des artistes qui ont participé aux enregistrements sur la dernière page de cette édition ; pour obtenir plus de renseignements, veuillez consulter notre site Internet : www.dowani.com.

Nous vous souhaitons beaucoup de plaisir à faire de la musique avec la collection *DOWANI 3 Tempi Play Along* et nous espérons que votre musicalité et votre application vous amèneront aussi rapidement que possible à la version de concert. Notre but est de vous offrir les bases nécessaires pour un travail efficace par la motivation et le plaisir.

Les Éditions DOWANI

Vorwort

Mit dieser Ausgabe stellen wir Ihnen leichte, aber musikalisch anspruchsvolle Bearbeitungen für Sopranblockflöte und Basso continuo vor. Manfredo Zimmermann, Professor für Blockflöte an der Musikhochschule Köln/Wuppertal und Spezialist für Alte Musik, hat die vorliegende Sammlung musikalischer Highlights aus verschiedenen Ländern herausgegeben und eingespielt. Die Basso-continuo-Begleitung ist bei den einzelnen Stücken unterschiedlich besetzt und wurde mit Cembalo oder Orgel eingespielt. Unsere Ausgabe ermöglicht es Ihnen, die Stücke systematisch und in drei verschiedenen Tempi mit professioneller Begleitung zu erarbeiten.

Auf der CD können Sie zuerst die Konzertversion eines jeden Stückes anhören (Blockflöte und Basso continuo). Nach dem Stimmen Ihres Instrumentes (Track 1) kann die musikalische Arbeit beginnen. Zum Üben folgt nun im langsamen und mittle-

ren Tempo die Basso-continuo- bzw. Orgelbegleitung, wobei im langsamen Tempo die Blockflöte als Orientierung leise im Hintergrund zu hören ist. Anschließend können Sie sich im Originaltempo begleiten lassen. Alle eingespielten Versionen wurden live aufgenommen. Die Namen der Künstler finden Sie auf der letzten Seite dieser Ausgabe; ausführlichere Informationen können Sie im Internet unter www.dowani.com nachlesen.

Wir wünschen Ihnen viel Spaß beim Musizieren mit unseren *DOWANI 3 Tempi Play Along*-Ausgaben und hoffen, dass Ihre Musikalität und Ihr Fleiß Sie möglichst bald bis zur Konzertversion führen werden. Unser Ziel ist es, Ihnen durch Motivation, Freude und Spaß die notwendigen Voraussetzungen für effektives Üben zu schaffen.

Ihr DOWANI Team

I

Rosa felice

M. F. Caroso (1527/35 – 1605)

DOW 1510

II

Ballo delle fiori

M. F. Caroso (1527/35 – 1605)

III

2 Menuette

J. S. Bach (1685 – 1750)

MENUETT I

ALBUM II

5 Easy Pieces for Descant (Soprano) Recorder and Basso continuo
by J. S. Bach, M. F. Caroso, H. Purcell, and A. Vivaldi

Descant (Soprano) Recorder / Flûte à bec soprano / Sopranblockflöte

DOWANI International

Recorder

I ②

Rosa felice

M. F. Caroso (1527/35 – 1605)

II ⑥

Ballo delle fiori

M. F. Caroso (1527/35 – 1605)

III ⑩

2 Menuette

J. S. Bach (1685 – 1750)

MENUETT I

DOW 1510

MENUETT II

IV ⑰

The Spring

A. Vivaldi (1678 – 1741)

4

Rondeau and Hornpipe

H. Purcell (1659 – 1695)

22 24 26

RONDEAU

23 25 27

HORNPIPE

MENUETT II

IV

The Spring

A. Vivaldi (1678 – 1741)
Piano Reduction: M. Zimmermann

V

Rondeau and Hornpipe

H. Purcell (1659 – 1695)

9

HORNPIPE

DOWANI CD:
- Track No. 1
- Track numbers in circles
- Track numbers in squares

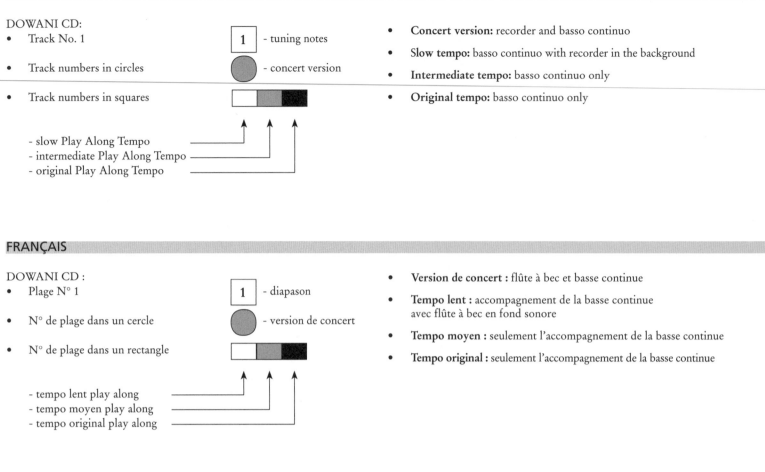

1 - tuning notes

- concert version

- slow Play Along Tempo
- intermediate Play Along Tempo
- original Play Along Tempo

- **Concert version:** recorder and basso continuo
- **Slow tempo:** basso continuo with recorder in the background
- **Intermediate tempo:** basso continuo only
- **Original tempo:** basso continuo only

DOWANI CD :
- Plage N° 1
- N° de plage dans un cercle
- N° de plage dans un rectangle

1 - diapason

- version de concert

- tempo lent play along
- tempo moyen play along
- tempo original play along

- **Version de concert :** flûte à bec et basse continue
- **Tempo lent :** accompagnement de la basse continue avec flûte à bec en fond sonore
- **Tempo moyen :** seulement l'accompagnement de la basse continue
- **Tempo original :** seulement l'accompagnement de la basse continue

DOWANI CD:
- Track Nr. 1
- Trackangabe im Kreis
- Trackangabe im Rechteck

1 - Stimmtöne

- Konzertversion

- langsames Play Along Tempo
- mittleres Play Along Tempo
- originales Play Along Tempo

- **Konzertversion:** Blockflöte und Basso continuo
- **Langsames Tempo:** Basso continuo mit Blockflöte im Hintergrund
- **Mittleres Tempo:** nur Basso continuo
- **Originaltempo:** nur Basso continuo

DOWANI - 3 Tempi Play Along is an imprint of:
De Haske (International) GmbH
Postfach 60, CH-6332 Hagendorn
Switzerland
Phone: +41-(0)41-784 30 84 / Fax: +41-(0)41-784 30 80
Email: info@dowani.com
www.dowani.com

Recording: Matthias Schlubeck, Germany
Digital Mastering: Traton GmbH, Switzerland
Project Supervisor: DraDoVision Est., Drazen Domjanic,
Liechtenstein (www.dradovision.com)

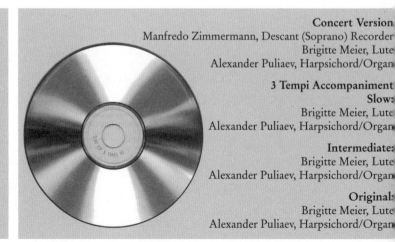

Concert Version
Manfredo Zimmermann, Descant (Soprano) Recorder
Brigitte Meier, Lute
Alexander Puliaev, Harpsichord/Organ

3 Tempi Accompaniment
Slow:
Brigitte Meier, Lute
Alexander Puliaev, Harpsichord/Organ

Intermediate:
Brigitte Meier, Lute
Alexander Puliaev, Harpsichord/Organ

Original:
Brigitte Meier, Lute
Alexander Puliaev, Harpsichord/Organ